Arianna Candell · Rosa M. Curto

Parties are a lot of fun!

Wow! Lots of kids are going to Mark's birthday party – it will be so much fun! When you're invited to somebody's house along with lots of other kids, you must be careful with all their belongings. If we all behave well, we can enjoy ourselves

Mark

Inviting people

Today is Mark's birthday party and he has asked his best friends over. He's invited all of his classmates too, so that no-one feels left out. Mark is feeling a bit nervous as it's almost time for the party. He wants his party to go really well.

Julia
Rosie
Lily
David

Getting ready

Lily has very long hair. She hates having it brushed or braided but she's promised her best friend Lucy that she will have her hair brushed and braided today for the party. She wants to look pretty for Mark's special day.

So many presents!

Mark has so many presents: storybooks, toys, and Julia even made him a special friendship bracelet. Rosie was so excited about Mark opening her present that she tore off the wrapping paper as she gave it to him! Now she wishes that she had let him unwrap his own present. It would have been more of a surprise for him.

Party time!

Once Mark has opened all his presents, the children have a great time playing party games. When it's time to eat, they all sit at the table with napkins on their laps. Adrian isn't sitting properly. He is kneeling on his chair so he can reach across the table.

Rosie

Adrian

Anna

Anna is sitting next to him and tells him to sit properly so he won't drop crumbs all over the floor. Adrian realises that Anna is right and sits down.

Have good table manners!

Lily

Peter is blowing bubbles in his drink and he's so hungry that he stuffs his mouth with food and then talks with his mouth full. He eats everything with his fingers and wipes his sticky hands on his T-shirt! Jim whispers something to his friend and Peter suddenly remembers his table manners. He unfolds his napkin, wipes his face, and picks up his fork.

Adrian
Lucy
Rachel
Maria
Jim
Peter

What a delicious-looking cake! As Mark closes his eyes to think of a wish, John almost blows out the candles. Julia stops him just in time and reminds John that it's not his birthday! It's Mark's birthday, so he's the only one who can make a wish and blow out the candles. It will be John's turn when it's his birthday.

Anna Peter

Who is blowing out the candles?

Mark
John
Julia

Rachel
Julia
Jim

May I have some more?

Mark has blown out his candles, so now everyone has a piece of birthday cake. Jim eats his in a flash and takes another piece. Rachel tells him to make sure that everyone has had a piece of cake first and that he should ask for a second helping. So Jim checks that everyone has a piece of cake on their plate and then he asks politely for a second piece.

Mark
Anna
Maria

No shouting

Mark's grandparents and his aunts and uncles have also come to his birthday party. The grown-ups don't like it when the children all talk loudly at the same time. Rachel and Maria keep shouting and squealing as they play together. Paul reminds them that they're in Mark's house and not the playground. Maria and Rachel didn't realise they were shouting. They play more quietly so that everyone can have a good time.

Rachel

Paul

No running inside

Paul and Mark are chasing each other up and down the hallway. Suddenly, there is a crash! They've knocked over a vase and some books. The kids all get a fright but luckily nothing is broken. Now all the kids understand why they can't run about inside the house. They can chase one another when they are in the park.

Paul

Mark

Adrian
Maria

Paul
Anna
Rosie
David

Cleaning Up

It's almost time to go home and soon all the mums and dads will come to pick up their children. What a mess! John has a good idea: If they all help to clean up, the job will get done really quickly. All the children help, and soon everything is back in order.

Julia
Paul
Peter
Mark
Rosie
Maria
Adrian
Lucy
Lily

Camera ready

Mark wants to have a photo taken with all his friends at his birthday party. Rosie doesn't like to have her photo taken, so she frowns at the camera! Mark laughs and tells her that she'll soon be sorry when she sees the photo. So in the next photo, Rosie makes sure she's smiling!

Thank you and goodbye

The party is over and it's time for the children to go. When Julia's parents come , she says she doesn't want to go home yet. She's having such fun, she wants to stay a bit longer. Rosie tells her it's time to go, and they can come back another day. Julia knows that her friend is right. She thanks Mark and his parents for inviting her to such a wonderful party and says goodbye.

Mark
Julia

Mark

What a party!

The party is finally over and everyone has gone home. Mark sits down and thinks about all the fun he's had with his family and friends. Everyone had such a good time. It's been the best day ever!

Activities

BALLOONS

It's nice to have balloons at your party. Get a variety of colourful balloons, and ask a grown-up to help you blow them up. Then use broad-tipped markers to draw funny faces on them. Your friends will say they are the best-looking balloons they've ever seen!

A PARTY HOST

Keep several things in mind when you are organising a birthday party. Parents usually prepare all the activities, but children can help in many ways and can also offer some good ideas of what children like.

HOT CHOCOLATE

When we invite friends to our house, we like to offer them something to eat and drink. Almost everyone enjoys a good cup of hot cocoa or chocolate. It's easy to make, but ask a grown-up to help you.

Follow these steps: Get all the ingredients together: milk, powdered cocoa or chocolate and sugar. Begin by pouring a little milk into each cup and then add some cocoa and sugar. Stir this mixture well. Then put enough milk into a pan and heat it (the quantity will depend on the number of people). Ask a grown-up to heat the milk until it starts to boil. Top up each cup with hot milk and stir to mix. It will now be ready to serve and share with your friends.

A CUP FOR EACH GUEST

When there are lots of people at a party, it's hard for everyone to keep track of their own cup. Try drawing a picture of each of your guests on the plastic or paper cups. You can write their names under the drawings as well.

SAYING THANK YOU

How can you say a special thank you to your guests for bringing you presents? Here is an idea: Make picture frames out of thick paper or card. Inside each frame you can tape a nice picture. Then add a little thank-you note for the gift that was given to you.
Ask a grown-up to help you cut out the frame if needed. Your friends will have a very nice surprise!

Guidelines for parents

GETTING READY

Getting ready to go to a party is an exciting part of the day. Explain to the children that it's important to look your best when you have been invited to a party or when meeting someone new. When we give a party or go to someone else's party, it's nice to see everyone looking their best.

WHEN CHILDREN PLAY TOGETHER

Children can get over-excited when they are with lots of other children, and it may be difficult for them to behave. Parties and get-togethers are usually noisy, but we can explain to the children that they can still have fun without shouting and running around. They must understand that they have to respect the host's property. Having some guidelines helps children play without adults constantly reminding them to behave.

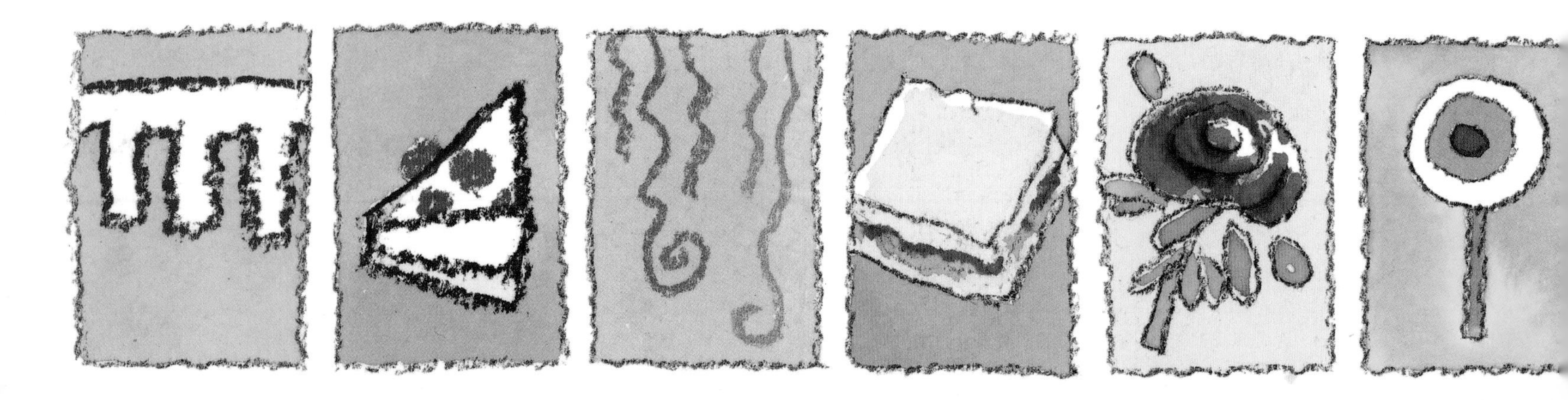

HELPFUL REMINDERS

Getting children ready to go out for special occasions or functions can seem to be an overwhelming task. Parents often worry about how their children will behave.

Many of the ideas presented in this book can help you to have an enjoyable and peaceful day (or at least as peaceful as possible). The suggestions about party behaviour can be extended to other occasions when we go out with our own children, to a restaurant, to visit grandparents, to a friend's house, to family parties and so forth. With a little initial explanation about good behaviour, going out with our children can be a more enjoyable experience. In your explanation, include what you will be doing, where you will go, who you will see, and so forth. Anticipate any misbehaviour that may occur, and let your children know what behaviour is unacceptable and why!

EATING MANNERS

Children may have been taught good table manners, but they often forget to use them when they are with other people. They may misbehave or act silly. Before going out, remind them that they should eat with their forks and wipe their mouth with a napkin. They should not talk with their mouth full, and they need to avoid silly behaviour such as blowing bubbles with their drinking straw! It is also important to remind them not to leave the table until they are excused. They should also ask politely if they may have a second helping.

Remind them that they should have good table manners at home as well as when they are at a party or a restaurant.

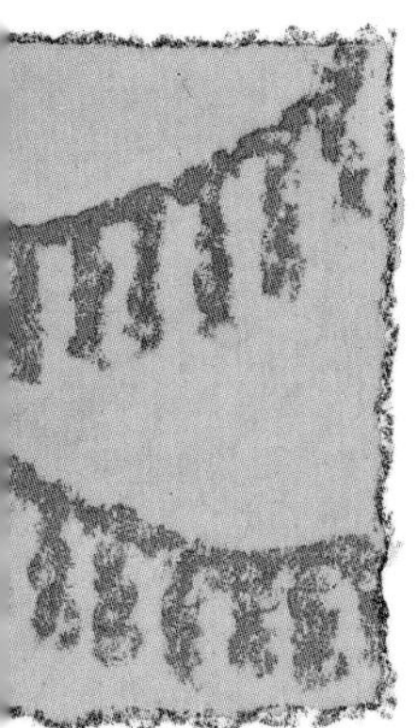
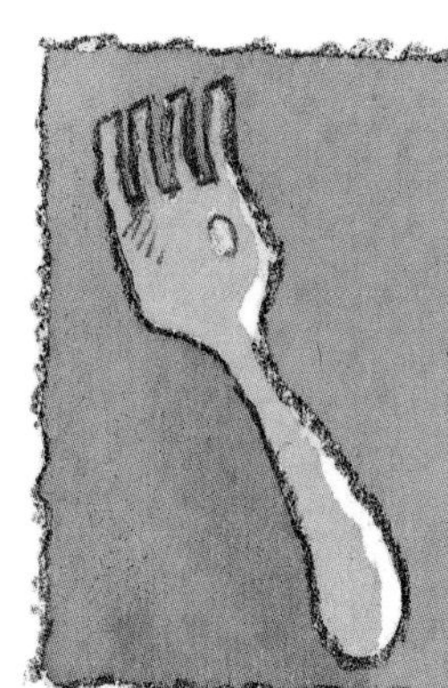

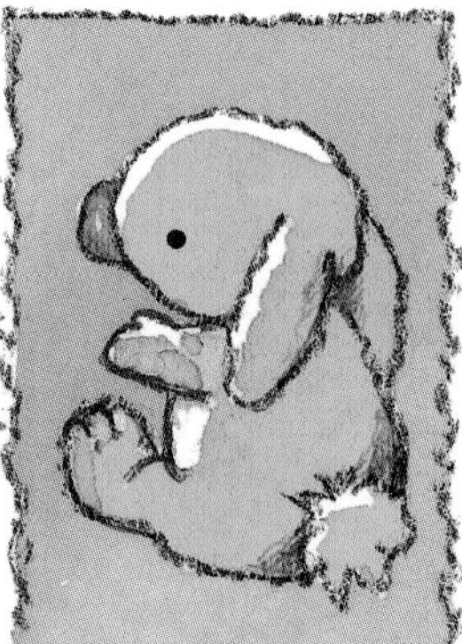

Published in Great Britain in MMXII by
Book House, an imprint of
The Salariya Book Company Ltd
25 Marlborough Place, Brighton BN1 1UB
www.salariya.com
www.book-house.co.uk

1 3 5 7 9 8 6 4 2

A CIP catalogue record for this book is available from the British Library.

Printed and bound in China.

PB ISBN: 978-1-908177-11-7

Original title of the book in Catalan: Com ens hem de comportar a les festes